San Francisco
August 19?

Prideaux Inc. Books
Palo alto, Calif.
Sherri - Joe Sawyer

Women's
N O T E S

Canadian representatives: General Publishing Co., Ltd.,
30 Lesmill Road, Don Mills, Ontario M3B 2T6.

ISBN 1–56138–481–X

Cover design by Toby Schmidt
Interior design by Lili Schwartz
Cover and interior illustrations by Valerie Coursen
Typography by Deborah Lugar
Printed in the United States

This book may be ordered by mail from the publisher.
Please add $1.00 for postage and handling.
But try your bookstore first!

Running Press Book Publishers
125 South Twenty-second Street
Philadelphia, Pennsylvania 19103–4399

Women's
NOTES

Running Press
Philadelphia • London

It's never too late to have a happy

childhood.

SHARI LEWIS, B. 1934
AMERICAN ENTERTAINER

Etiquette has us behaving very often much better than we genuinely feel.

Judith Martin (Miss Manners), b. 1938
American writer

Everyone should have a chance at a breathtaking piece of folly at least once in his life.

Elizabeth Taylor, b. 1932
American actress

There is so much in the world for us all if we only have the eyes to see it, and the heart to love it, and the hand to gather it to ourselves. . . .

The first "dream of success" is a part of
our youth. To start over after failing
the initial dream is a part of our
maturing process.

KATHLEEN DE AZEVEDO, B. 1955
BRAZILIAN-BORN AMERICAN POET

$\mathcal{S}$uccess for me is having ten

honeydew melons and eating only

the top half of each one.

Barbra Streisand, b. 1942
American singer, actress, and director

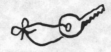

No one is experienced . . .

until he gets there.

Shirley Temple Black, b. 1928
American Ambassador to the U.N.

We love to work because work
gives us genuine happiness, the
posting and solving of problems,
the joyful exercise of the
imagination.

Joyce Carol Oates, b. 1938
American writer

I prefer adventure
to comfort.

PRINCESS STEPHANIE
OF MONACO, B. 1965

Sleeping is very underrated.

SUZY BECKER
20TH-CENTURY AMERICAN WRITER
AND ILLUSTRATOR

If you obey all the rules you miss

all the fun.

Katharine Hepburn, b. 1909
American actress

Never economize on luxuries.

Angela Thirkell (1890–1961)
British writer

I'd rather have roses on my table

than diamonds on my neck.

Emma Goldman (1869–1940)
Russian-born American activist

The hardest years in life are those

between ten and seventy.

Helen Hayes (1900–1993)
American actress

. . . we get to a certain age, and then the rest of our lives we
do everything we can to get back to the way we were when
we were little . . . using wisdom to come back to innocence.

Kate Bush, b. 1958
English singer-songwriter

Whenever truth is spoken
there is somewhere an increase of
understanding and faith.

Pearl Bailey (1918–1990)
American entertainer

Seldom, very seldom does complete truth belong to any human disclosure; seldom can it happen that something is not a little disguised, or a little mistaken. . . .

Jane Austen (1775–1817)
English writer

*S*he had always been too wise to tell him all she thought and felt, knowing by some intuition of her own womanhood that no man wants to know everything of any woman.

Pearl S. Buck (1892–1973)
American writer

Like a Russian doll nesting ever

smaller dolls inside of it, I house

an infinity of selves.

Daphne Merkin
20th-century American writer

Women are never what they seem to be. There is the woman you see
and the woman who is hidden.

Erma Bombeck, b. 1927
American writer

The mind fits the world and shapes it
as a river fits and shapes its own banks.

ANNIE DILLARD, B. 1945
AMERICAN WRITER

. . . love is a great beautifier.

Louisa May Alcott (1832–1888)
American writer and editor

$\mathcal{B}$eauty doesn't hold still but changes with the seasons. You have it no matter what season you're in.

KAVLAN PICKFORD, B. 1930
AMERICAN MODEL, WRITER, AND LECTURER

Wild nights are my glory. . . .

Madeleine L'Engle, b. 1918
American writer

Love isn't the dying moan of a distant

violin; it's the triumphant twang

of a bedspring.

MARY MARTIN, B. 1913
AMERICAN ENTERTAINER

Do not seek the because—*in love
there is no because, no reason, no
explanation, no solutions.*

Anaïs Nin (1903–1977)
French-born American writer

The loss of young first love is so painful that it borders on the ludicrous.

Maya Angelou, b. 1928
American writer

There is nothing ridiculous in love.

OLIVE SCHREINER (1855–1920)
SOUTH AFRICAN WRITER, FEMINIST,
AND SOCIAL CRITIC

. . . love . . . plunges us into our darkest
histories and then brings us back up
still breathing, with artifacts
to show for ourselves.

Rachel Srubas, b. 1964
American poet

. . . love, any sort of love, even of poetry, no matter what beautiful-true perfection it gets up to, forgets at its peril the nuzzling, butting, pie-eyed clay in which the foot of its ladder had better be secured.

George Eliot [Mary Ann Evans] (1819–1880)
English writer

It is odd how we sometimes deny ourselves the very pleasure we have longed for and which is finally within our reach.

CYNTHIA RYLANT, B. 1954
AMERICAN WRITER

Love each other to a crisp.

Alexandra Stoddard
20th-century American writer

When one is a stranger to oneself then

one is estranged from others too.

Anne Morrow Lindbergh, b. 1906
American writer

If we want a love message to be heard, it has got to be sent out. To keep a lamp burning, we have to keep putting oil in it.

Mother Teresa, b. 1910
Albanian cleric

. . . the soul and the spirit have resources that are astonishing. Like
wolves and other creatures, the soul and spirit are able to thrive on very
little, and sometimes for a long time on nothing. To me, it is the miracle
of miracles that this is so.

CLARISSA PINKOLA ESTES
20TH-CENTURY AMERICAN ANALYST AND WRITER

How we spend our days is, of

course, how we spend our lives.

Annie Dillard, b. 1945
American writer

*T*he sacred is not in the sky, the place of transcendent, abstract principle, but rather is based on this earth, in the ordinary dwelling places of our lives, in our gardens and kitchens and bedrooms.

MARILYN SEWELL, B. 1941
AMERICAN CLERIC

A world is to be fought for,

sung, and built:

Love must imagine the world.

Muriel Rukeyser (1913–1980)
American poet

The future belongs to those who believe

in the beauty of their dreams.

Eleanor Roosevelt (1884–1962)
American stateswoman and humanitarian